Disney · PIXAR

Cars 3

Race On!

PaRragon

Bath · New York · Cologne · Melbourne · Delhi
Hong Kong · Shenzhen · Singapore

This edition published by Parragon Books Ltd in 2017

Parragon Books Ltd
Chartist House
15–17 Trim Street
Bath BA1 1HA, UK
www.parragon.com

ISBN 978-1-4748-7190-7

Printed in China

Racing hero

Rev up your imagination and give Lightning an awesome new look. Doodle some daring designs, and then add super-cool colours.

Perfect paint job

Lightning and the other cars are getting a paint job touch-up before the next big race. Draw lines to connect the correct design detail to each car.

Answers on page 47

Lightning maze

Lightning McQueen is training hard on the track. Using the key to help you, follow the lightning bolts to guide him to the finish line.

Answer on page 47

KEY

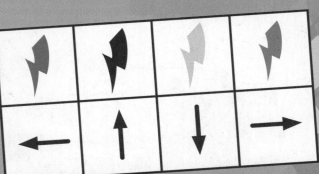

Start

Finish

6

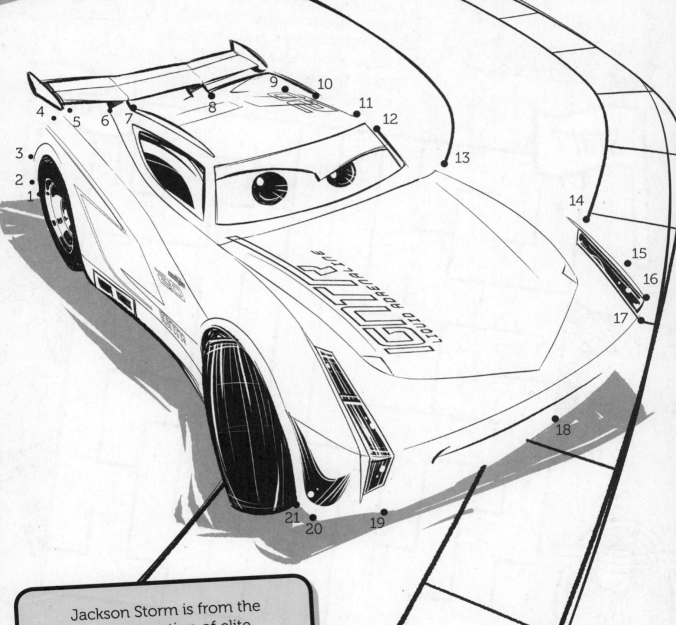

Jackson Storm is from the
next generation of elite
racers – he's young, fast,
and he wants to win!
Connect the dots to get Storm
race-ready, and then add colour.

Champion racers

Complete this maze with a friend, choosing who will be Lightning McQueen and who will be Jackson Storm. Whoever finishes the maze first wins!

Start

Start

Finish

.... is the winner!

Answers on page 47

Cruz code

Cruz is setting up the high-tech simulator to test Lightning's top speed, but first she needs to crack this code. Use the key below to reveal the hidden message.

Key

A	C	E	G	N	R	T	X

			_								

Stylish Sterling

Sterling is cool and calm when it comes to business. Colour in the picture of him above to match his style, or give him a new look!

Speedy sudoku

Test your brainpower by using the code to finish this awesome grid. Write the correct letter in each square. There should be one of each picture in every horizontal row and vertical column.

Code | A | B | C | D

Top speed

Look at Lightning McQueen's speedometer. Can you circle the two other speedometers that show the same speed?

195
MAXIMUM SPEED
LMQ
TOP SPEED

A

185
MAXIMUM SPEED
LMQ
TOP SPEED

B

195
MAXIMUM SPEED
LMQ
TOP SPEED

C

195
MAXIMUM SPEED
LMQ
TOP SPEED

E

95
MAXIMUM SPEED
LMQ
TOP SPEED

D

50
MAXIMUM SPEED
LMQ
TOP SPEED

F

165
MAXIMUM SPEED
LMQ
TOP SPEED

Answers on page 47

Legends of the track

Doc Hudson, Louise Nash and Lightning McQueen are all racing heroes. Write the name of each champion under the correct shadow and then colour in the racing flag next to it.

1

2

3

Answers on page 47

Damage differences

Can you spot five differences between these two pictures of Dr Damage?
Colour in a cone for each difference you find.

Answers on page 47

Draw Smokey

Using the top picture as a guide, draw Smokey and then colour him in.

Race ready

Help Lightning through the maze to the pit stop, collecting the items he needs along the way.

Start

Finish

Answer on page 47

Derby disaster

Look at these close-up snaps from the demolition derby. Can you draw lines to match each character with their picture?

Racing role model

Which of the awesome racing legends are you most like? Take this cool quiz to find out!

What is your best skill?

A Speed **B** Leadership **C** Intelligence **D** Giving advice

Which of these words describes you best?

A Cool **B** Brave **C** Tough **D** Smart

If you were a car, what would your design be?

A Super-fast and powerful   **B** Classic and reliable

C High-tech and modern   **D** Stylish and sleek

The best thing about being a racer is...

A Winning   **B** Being a hero

C Being part of a team   **D** Making money

MOSTLY As

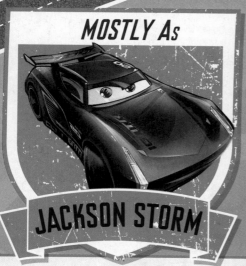

JACKSON STORM

You're tough, powerful and a bit of a rebel. You are always focused on winning and will do anything to get there.

MOSTLY Bs

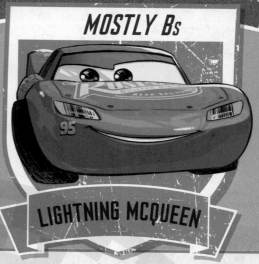

LIGHTNING MCQUEEN

Like Lightning McQueen, you're the hero of the track and you train hard. Winning is great, but friends are more important.

MOSTLY Cs

CRUZ RAMIREZ

You're a natural leader with a great sense of adventure. You like to use new technology, and your team can always count on you.

MOSTLY Ds

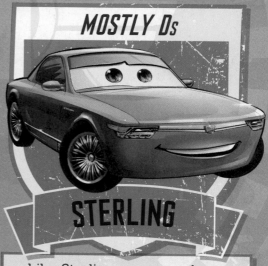

STERLING

Like Sterling, you are clever and good at thinking practically. Your team looks to you for help and guidance.

Perfect puzzle

Draw lines to match the missing pieces to the correct place in the puzzle. Race on!

Answers on page 47

Odd one out

The Thunder Hollow Speedway racers love creating mayhem on the track. Spot the odd one out in each row.

1 **2** **3** **4**

Arvy

Miss Fritter

Dr Damage

Taco

Answers on page 47

Fearless Fritter

Miss Fritter isn't afraid to cause some serious damage.
Drive your way through the maze and knock
out your competition along the way!

Start

Finish

Answer on page 47

Custom car

Design and draw your own awesome car here!

Come up with your own race-ready name.

Cool colouring

Cruz has always dreamed of being a racer. Use your favourite colours to give her a brand-new look that will stand out on the track!

Spot the difference

Circle the five differences between these pictures
of Lightning McQueen and his race rivals.
Colour in a flag for every difference you spot!

Race time!

There's a new generation of racers revving up! Trace their paths without taking your pencil off the paper or touching the sides, and count the flags as you go. The car with the most flags is the winner!

Answers on page 48

Number of flags:

Number of flags:

Number of flags:

Number of flags:

Mack maze

Help Lightning reach Mack by finding the right route through the maze.

Answer on page 48

Pit-stop patterns

Which picture comes next in each row?
Work out the pattern and write the
correct letter in each circle.

A
B
C
D
E

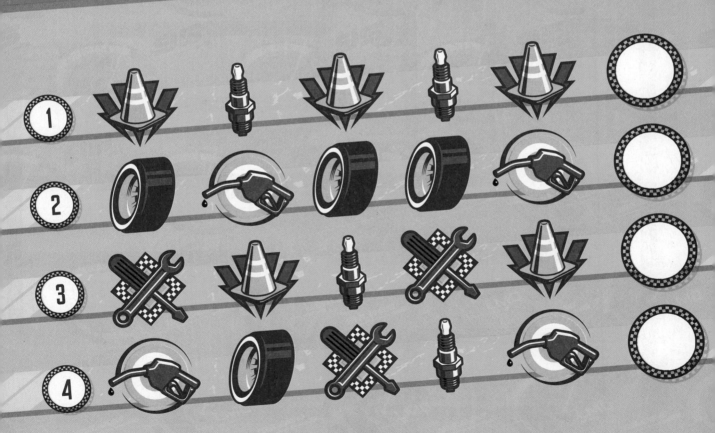

1

2

3

4

Lightning McQueen and Cruz have entered a demolition derby by mistake! Guide them through the maze to safety, avoiding the other cars.

Finish

Answer on page 48

195

MAXIMUM SPEED

LMQ
TOP SPEED

Start

Spelling legend

Trace the letters to spell the names
of the four racing legends below.

Louise

River

Rusty

Junior

Storm trail

Jackson Storm is on a winning streak!
Find the trail that will lead him to another trophy.

Answers on page 48

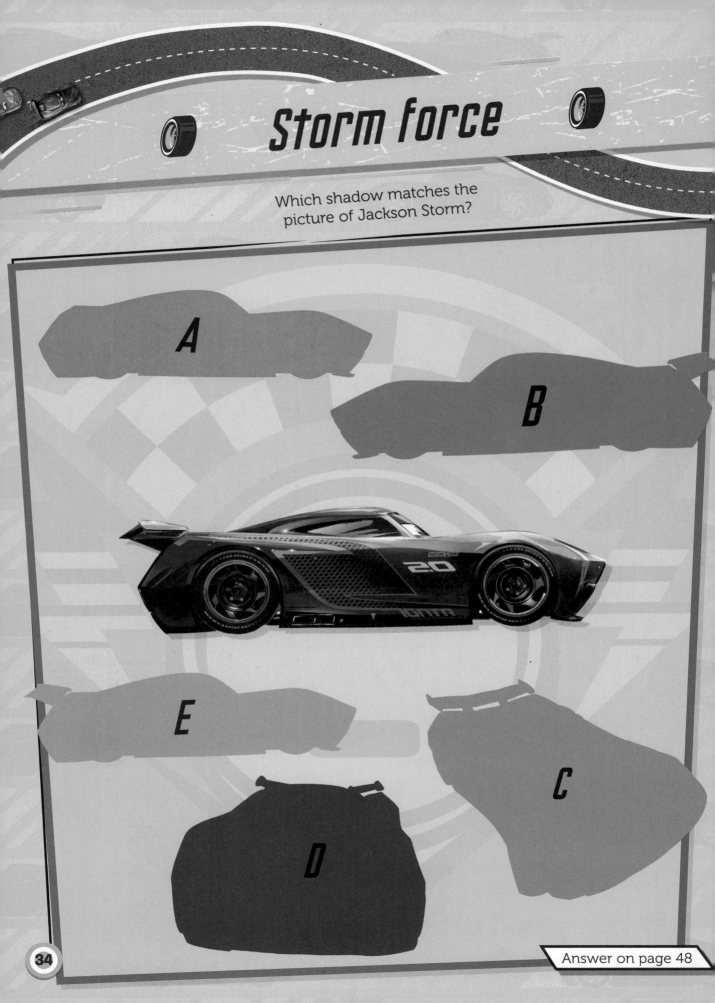

Storm force

Which shadow matches the picture of Jackson Storm?

A

B

E

C

D

Answer on page 48

Pile-up pals

Uh-oh! There's been a pile-up at the demolition derby.
Can you answer the questions below?

1 How many cars can you count?

2 Which character is next to Taco at the bottom of the pile-up?

3 Who is underneath Arvy?

4 How many wheels can you count that aren't attached to cars?

Car close-ups

There are always lots of photographers at the Piston Cup, but sometimes they get a bit too close! Can you match the characters to their close-ups?

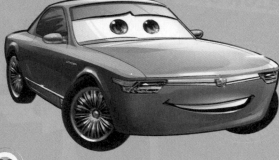

Answers on page 48

Crew colouring

A race champion is nothing without his trusty pit crew! Colour in this picture of Luigi and Guido.

Rust-eze refresh

You've bought out Rust-eze and are now Lightning McQueen's sponsor! Draw a new logo for your company below.

Medicated
Rust·eze
BUMPER OINTMENT
REAR END FORMULA

Counting Cruz

Cruz is intelligent, hard-working and above all, FAST. Can you keep up with her? Count how many times you can spot Cruz below.

How many pictures of Cruz do you see?

Answer on page 48

Draw your trailer

What would your trailer look like if you were a racing car? Design it on the back of Mack!

Circle every other letter from the spiral below
to reveal what Rusty is saying to Lightning McQueen.
The first one has been done for you.

D _ _ _   _ _ _ _ _ _

_ _ _   _ _ _ _ !

Perfect pairs

With a friend, cover each car with a piece of paper then take it in turns to remove a piece from each page. If the two uncovered cars match, call 'snap!' and keep the pieces of paper. If they don't, replace the paper and keep playing until all the pairs have been found!

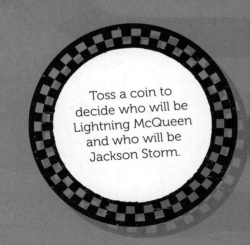

Toss a coin to decide who will be Lightning McQueen and who will be Jackson Storm.

Circle one of your player cars each time you match a pair!

Jackson Storm:

Lightning McQueen:

Numbers never lie

Natalie Certain uses numbers to predict who is going to win each race! Help her by adding up the numbers next to each racer. Award the trophy to the one with the highest number.

Jackson Storm

$$5 + 2 =$$

Cruz

$$3 + 7 =$$

Lightning McQueen

$$4 + 5 =$$

And the winner is:

....

Answers on page 48

Training hard

Design an awesome racetrack for Lightning and Cruz to zoom around. Don't forget to draw the finish line!

Racing heroes

Draw lines to link these racers to their shadows.

Answers on page 48

ANSWERS

Page 5

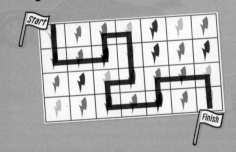

Page 6

Page 8

Page 9
NEXT-GEN RACER

Page 11

D		A	
	D	B	A
B		C	
			D

Page 12
B & C

Page 13
1. Doc Hudson
2. Louise Nash
3. Lightning McQueen

Page 14

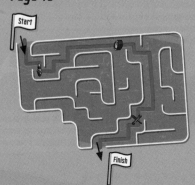

Page 16

Page 17

Page 20

Page 21
Arvy – 2, Miss Fritter – 3,
Dr. Damage – 1, Taco – 4

Page 22

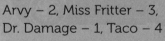

Page 25

Page 26-27
A – 5, B – 2, C – 4, D – 6

Page 28

Page 29
1 – A, 2 – D, 3 – A, 4 – D

Page 30-31

Page 33

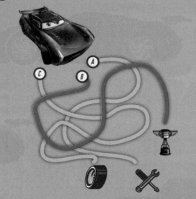

Page 34
The matching shadow is E.

Page 35
1 – six, 2 – Cruz, 3 – Lightning McQueen, 4 – five

Page 36

Page 39
11

Page 41
DOC WOULD BE PROUD!

Page 44
Jackson Storm – 7
Cruz – 10
Lightening McQueen – 9

The winner is Cruz!

Page 46